B55 025 972 8

KU-545-427

Three Little Kittehs

and other animal rhymes

Miles Kelly

Mary's Lamb

Mary had a little lamb,
Its fleece was white as snow,
And everywhere that Mary went
The lamb was sure to go.

It followed her to school one day,
Which was against the rule,
It made the children laugh and play
To see a lamb at school.

$2 \times 1 = 2$
$2 \times 2 = 4$
$2 \times 3 = 6$
$2 \times 4 = 8$
$2 \times 5 = 10$
$\times 6 = 12$

And so the teacher turned it out,
But still it lingered near,
And waited patiently about
Till Mary did appear.

"Why does the lamb love Mary so?"
The eager children cry;
"Why, Mary loves the lamb, you know,"
The teacher did reply.

$4 + 4 = 8$

$6 = 12$

$3 + 2 = 5$

$4 + 5 = ?$

Little Tommy Tittlemouse

Little Tommy Tittlemouse
Lived in a little house;
He caught fishes
In other mens' ditches.

Ride a Cock Horse

Ride a cock horse to Banbury Cross,
To see a fine lady upon a white horse;
Rings on her fingers and bells on her toes,
And she shall have music wherever she goes.

Oh Where Oh Where has my Little Dog Gone?

Oh where, oh where
Has my little dog gone?
Oh where, oh where can he be?

With his ears cut short
And his tail cut long
Oh where, oh where can he be?

Pussy cat, Pussy cat

Pussy cat, pussy cat, where have you been?

I've been up to London to visit the queen!

Pussy cat, pussy cat, what did you there?

I frightened a little mouse under the chair!

The Turtle

There was a little turtle
Who lived in a box.

He swam in the puddles
And climbed on the rocks.

He snapped at the mosquito,
He snapped at the flea.

He snapped at the minnow,
And he snapped at me.

He caught the mosquito,
He caught the flea.

He caught the minnow,
But he didn't catch me!

Pussy Cat Mole

Pussy cat Mole
Jumped over a coal,
And in her best petticoat
Burnt a great hole.

Poor pussy cat's weeping
She'll have no more milk
Until her best petticoat's
Mended with silk.

The North Wind Doth Blow

The North wind doth blow
and we shall have snow,
And what will poor robin do then,
Poor thing?

He'll sit in a barn
and keep himself warm
And hide his head under his wing,
Poor thing.

Three Little Kittens

Three little kittens, they lost their mittens,
And they began to cry,
"Oh mother dear, we sadly fear,
That we have lost our mittens."
"What! Lost your mittens, you naughty kittens!
Then you shall have no pie.
Meow, meow, meow.
Then you shall have no pie."

The three little kittens, they found their mittens,
And they began to cry,
"Oh mother dear, see here, see here,
For we have found our mittens."
"Put on your mittens, you silly kittens,
And you shall have some pie."
"Purr, purr, purr
Oh, let us have some pie."

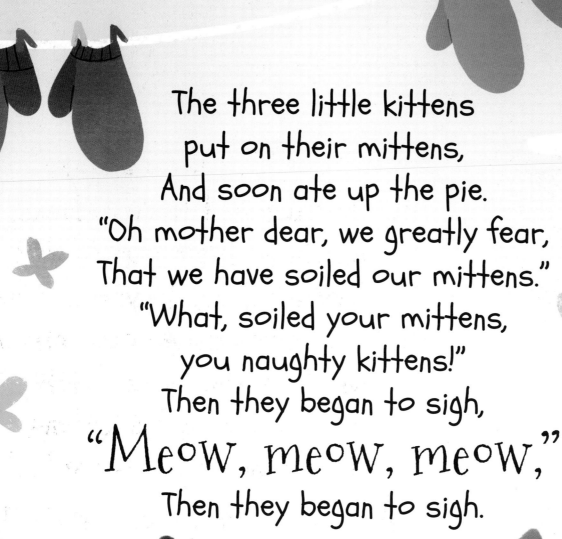

The three little kittens
put on their mittens,
And soon ate up the pie.
"Oh mother dear, we greatly fear,
That we have soiled our mittens."
"What, soiled your mittens,
you naughty kittens!"
Then they began to sigh,
"Meow, meow, meow,"
Then they began to sigh.

The three little kittens,
they washed their mittens,
And hung them out to dry.
"Oh mother dear, do you not hear,
That we have washed our mittens?"
"What, washed your mittens,
then you're good kittens,
But I smell a rat close by."
"Meow, meow, meow,
We smell a rat close by."

Old Mother Hubbard

Old Mother Hubbard
Went to the cupboard

To get her poor dog a bone.

But when she got there
The cupboard was bare,
So the poor dog had none.

Six Little Mice

Six little mice sat down to spin,
Pussy cat passed and she peeped in.
"What are you doing, my little men?"
"Weaving coats for gentlemen."

"Shall I come in and cut off your threads?"
"No, no, pussy cat, you'd bite off our heads."
"Oh, no, I'll not. I'll help you to spin."
"That may be so, but you don't come in."

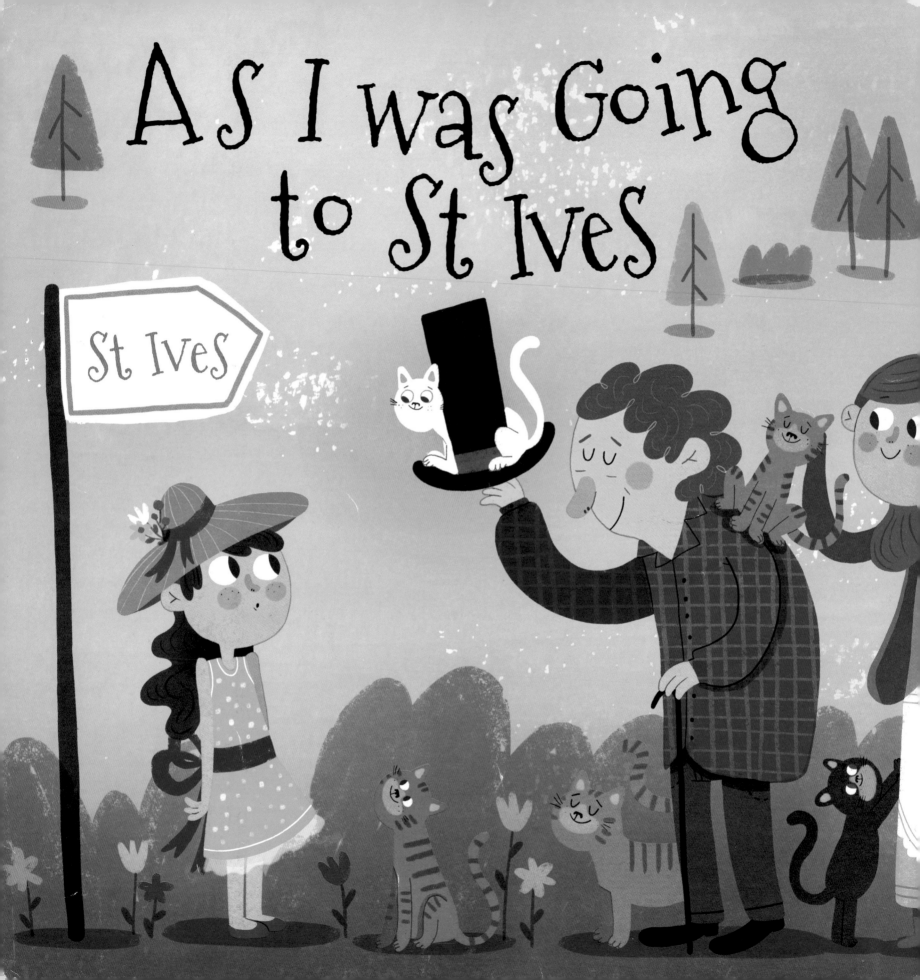

As I was Going to St Ives

As I was going to St Ives,
I met a man with seven wives,
Each wife had seven sacks,
Each sack had seven cats,
Each cat had seven kits:
Kits, cats, sacks, and wives,
How many were there
going to St Ives?

Ladybird, Ladybird

Ladybird, ladybird fly away home,
Your house is on fire and your children are gone,
All except one, and her name is Ann,
And she hid under the frying pan.